MATHS masterpieces

Maths skills + puzzles = art masterpieces

Gunter Schymkiw

Published by Prim-Ed Publishing
www.prim-ed.com

6007C

MATHS MASTERPIECES *(Middle)*

Published by Prim-Ed Publishing 2006

Reprinted under licence by Prim-Ed Publishing 2006

Copyright© Gunter Schymkiw 2005

ISBN 1 84654 018 6

PR–6007

Additional titles available in this series:
MATHS MASTERPIECES *(Upper)*

Internet websites

In some cases, websites or specific URLs may be recommended. While these are checked and rechecked at the time of publication, the publisher has no control over any subsequent changes which may be made to webpages. It is *strongly* recommended that the class teacher checks *all* URLs before allowing pupils to access them.

View all pages online

Website: www.prim-ed.com
Email: sales@prim-ed.com

FOREWORD

The activities in *Maths Masterpieces (Middle)* integrate mathematics with aspects of visual arts. As well as being provided with opportunities to consolidate knowledge and skills in mathematics, pupils are introduced to significant works of art and their artists.

Maths Masterpieces (Middle) aims to enhance children's appreciation of the works of great artists at the same time allowing them to build mathematical skills.

Other titles include: *Maths Masterpieces (Upper)*

CONTENTS

TEACHER INFORMATION

Each selected artwork is paired with a mathematical concept, in a group of three pages.

Page 1 of each group consists of a teachers page. Each teachers page contains the following information.

The **mathematical concept** being covered is indicated at the top of the page.

The **artwork and artist** to which this page relates is given.

Background information includes information about the artist, his/her style, influences and other artworks.

A picture of the **completed artwork** shows pupils the correct answers to their mathematical activity.

The **Internet image search** encourages teachers and pupils to more broadly appreciate the works of individual artists.

A '**Talking mathematically**' section is included with each activity. This provides lesson format suggestions, discusses possible mathematical emphases and provides further interesting background information that is both instructional and historical in its nature.

Occasionally, **additional activities** are given which may extend the activity into other learning areas such as English.

Pupil instructions explain how to complete the activity.

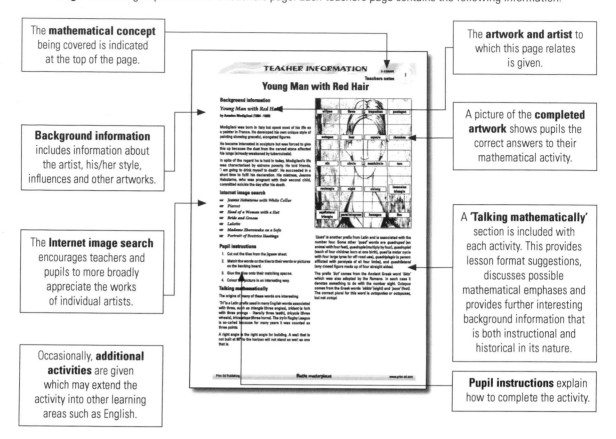

Page 2 of each group consists of the pupil activity page with the mathematical problems to be solved.

The **mathematical concept** being covered is indicated at the top of the page.

The **artwork** to which this page relates is given.

The **sums/problems** for the pupils to complete are provided.

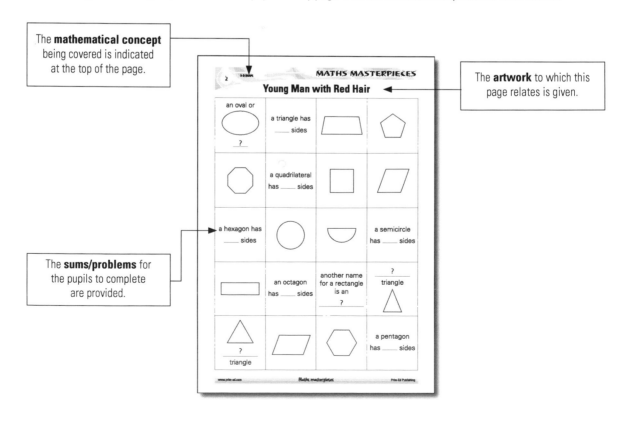

Page 3 of each group provides the answers to the sums/problems on 'mixed up' sections of the masterpiece.

The **mathematical concept** being covered is indicated at the top of the page.

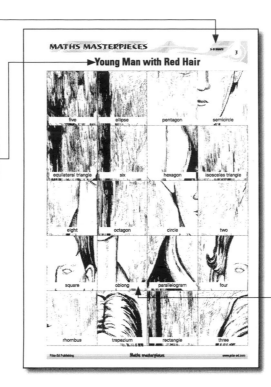

The **artwork** to which this page relates is given.

Answers for the sums/problems are given on the sections of the masterpiece. These sections will give a completed picture of the masterpiece once glued in the correct position.

CURRICULUM LINKS – MATHS

Activity	Country	Maths strand	Level	Objective
Young Man with Red Hair	England	Shape and space	Year 3	• classify 2–D shapes • refer to properties such as number of sides
			Year 4	• describe 2–D shapes • recognise equilateral and isosceles triangles
	Northern Ireland	Shape and space	KS 2	• name 2–D shapes • classify shapes through examination of sides
	Republic of Ireland	Shape and space	3rd/4th	• identify and classify 2–D shapes • explore the properties (sides) of 2–D shapes
	Scotland	Shape	B	• respond to descriptions which refer to sides of shapes
			D	• recognise pentagons and hexagons • identify equilateral and isosceles triangles
	Wales	Shape and space	KS 2	• recognise geometrical features and properties of 2–D shapes
Colour Theory	England	Measures	Year 3	• begin to use decimal notation for centimetres
		Number	Year 4	• understand decimal notation and place value for tenths
	Northern Ireland	Measures	KS 2	• use addition to solve problems involving measures and decimals
	Republic of Ireland	Measures	3rd/4th	• complete practical tasks involving the addition of units of length
		Number	4th	• add whole numbers and decimals

Activity	Country	Maths strand	Level	Objective
Colour Theory	Scotland	Number	C/D	• add measurements
	Wales	Number	KS 2	• add decimals • use addition to solve problems involving measures
Linear Perspective	England	Measures	Year 3	• read time to five minutes on an analogue and digital clock
	Northern Ireland	Measures	KS 2	• recognise times on the analogue clock to five minute intervals • read analogue and digital displays and understand the relationship between them
	Republic of Ireland	Measures	3rd	• read time in five–minute intervals on analogue and digital clocks
	Scotland	Measurement	B	• tell time using analogue displays • read time in hours and minutes using digital displays
	Wales	Measures	KS 2	• use appropriate measuring instruments to read to an increasing degree of accuracy
Still Life with Apples	England	Measures	Year 3 Year 3/4	• know relationships between units of time • use and read the vocabulary related to time
	Northern Ireland	Measures	KS 2	• know units of measurement of time and the relationship between them • know the months of the year and explore calendar patterns
	Republic of Ireland	Measures	3rd/4th	• consolidate and develop a sense of time passing
	Scotland	Measurement	B	• place events in time sequences
	Wales	Measures	KS 2	• extend understanding of relationship between units (of time)
Jonah and the Whale	England	Calculations	Year 3	• use known number facts and place value to add mentally
	Northern Ireland	Number	KS 2	• add mentally two two-digit numbers up to 100
	Republic of Ireland	Number	2nd	• add numbers within 99 without renaming
	Scotland	Number	B	• add two-digit numbers without a calculator
	Wales	Number	KS 2	• add integers without a calculator
Monarch of the Glen	England	Calculations	Year 3	• begin to use column addition where the calculation cannot easily be done mentally
	Northern Ireland	Number	KS 2	• add mentally two two-digit numbers up to 100
	Republic of Ireland	Number	2nd	• add numbers within 99 with renaming
	Scotland	Number	B	• add two-digit numbers without a calculator
	Wales	Number	KS 2	• add integers without a calculator
Ancient Cave Painting	England	Calculations	Year 3	• add three two-digit numbers
	Northern Ireland	Number	KS 2	• develop a range of non-calculator methods of computation
	Republic of Ireland	Number	3rd	• add, with renaming, within 999
	Scotland	Number	B	• add two-digit numbers without a calculator
	Wales	Number	KS 2	• add integers without a calculator

Activity	Country	Maths strand	Level	Objective
The Haywain	England	Shape and space	Year 3	• refer to properties of 3–D shapes (faces, edges, vertices)
			Year 3/4	• classify and describe 3–D shapes
	Northern Ireland	Shape and space	KS 2	• name and describe 3–D shapes • investigate the number of faces, edges and vertices on 3–D shapes
	Republic of Ireland	Shape and space	3rd	• explore the properties of 3–D shapes (faces, edges, corners)
			3rd/4th	• identify and classify 3–D shapes
	Scotland	Shape	C	• recognise 3–D shapes from 2–D drawings
			D	• discuss 3–D shapes, referring to faces, edges and vertices
	Wales	Shape and space	KS 2	• recognise geometrical features and properties of 3–D shapes
Henry VIII	England	Calculations	Year 3	• use known number facts and place value to subtract mentally
	Northern Ireland	Number	KS 2	• subtract mentally one two-digit number from another
	Republic of Ireland	Number	2nd	• subtract numbers without renaming within 99
	Scotland	Number	B	• subtract two-digit numbers without a calculator
	Wales	Number	KS 2	• subtract integers without a calculator
The Sleep of Reason Produces Monsters	England	Shape and space	Year 3	• identify and sketch lines of symmetry in simple shapes
			Year 4	• classify shapes according to right angles and symmetry properties • recognise horizontal and vertical lines • know one right angle is 90°
			Year 5	• recognise reflective symmetry in regular shapes • recognise perpendicular and parallel lines • identify acute and obtuse angles
	Northern Ireland	Shape and space	KS 2	• look for line symmetry • find right angles in 2–D shapes • develop language associated with line and angle • recognise properties of acute, obtuse and reflex angles • investigate angles in 2–D shapes
	Republic of Ireland	Shape and space	3rd	• identify and draw lines of symmetry in 2–D shapes • identify and classify vertical, horizontal and parallel lines
			4th	• identify and classify oblique and perpendicular lines
			3rd/4th	• classify angles as greater than, less than or equal to a right angle
	Scotland	Shape	B	• find lines of symmetry in 2–D shapes • know that a right angle is 90° • use right, acute and obtuse to describe angles • know that a straight angle is 180°
	Wales	Shape and space	KS 2	• recognise reflective symmetry in 2–D shapes • use right angles • use language of angles

CURRICULUM LINKS – MATHS

Activity	Country	Maths strand	Level	Objective
The Milkmaid	England	Calculations	Year 3	• begin to use column subtraction where the calculation cannot easily be done mentally
	Northern Ireland	Number	KS 2	• develop non-calculator methods of subtraction
	Republic of Ireland	Number	2nd	• subtract numbers with renaming within 99
	Scotland	Number	B	• subtract two-digit numbers without a calculator
	Wales	Number	KS 2	• subtract integers without a calculator
Bubbles	England	Calculations	Year 3	• know multiplication facts for 2 and 5 times-tables and begin to know 3 and 4 times-tables • use known number facts and place value to carry out mentally simple multiplications
			Year 4	• develop written methods for TU x U • know multiplication facts for 2, 3, 4 and 5 times-tables
	Northern Ireland	Number	KS 2	• know multiplication facts • develop non-calculator methods of computation
	Republic of Ireland	Number	3rd/4th	• develop and recall multiplication facts • multiply a two-digit number by a one-digit number
	Scotland	Number	B	• multiply mentally by 2, 3, 4 and 5 • multiply without a calculator for two-digit numbers multiplied by 2, 3, 4 or 5
	Wales	Number	KS 2	• know multiplication facts • develop informal written methods of multiplication
Blue Horses	England	Calculations	Year 3	• know multiplication facts for 2 and 5 times-tables and begin to know 3 and 4 times-tables • use known number facts and place value to carry out mentally simple multiplications
			Year 4	• develop written methods for TU x U • know multiplication facts for 2, 3, 4 and 5 times-tables
	Northern Ireland	Number	KS 2	• know multiplication facts • develop non-calculator methods of computation
	Republic of Ireland	Number	3rd/4th	• develop and recall multiplication facts
			4th	• multiply a three-digit number by a one-digit number
	Scotland	Number	B	• multiply mentally by 2, 3, 4 and 5
			C	• multiply three-digit whole numbers by one-digit whole number
	Wales	Number	KS 2	• know multiplication facts • develop informal written methods of multiplication
The Gulf Stream	England	Calculations	Year 4	• know multiplication facts for 2, 3, 4, 5 and 10 times-tables and begin to know multiplication facts for 6, 7, 8 and 9 times-tables • use known number facts and place value to multiply • develop written methods for TU x U
	Northern Ireland	Number	KS 2	• know multiplication facts • develop non-calculator methods of computation
	Republic of Ireland	Number	3rd/4th	• develop and recall multiplication facts within 100 • multiply a two-digit number by a one-digit number
	Scotland	Number	C	• multiply within the confines of all tables to 10 • multiply two-digit whole numbers by any single-digit whole number without a calculator
	Wales	Number	KS 2	• know multiplication facts • develop informal written methods of multiplication

CURRICULUM LINKS – MATHS

Activity	Country	Maths strand	Level	Objective
The Laughing Cavalier	England	Calculations	Year 3/4	• derive division facts corresponding to the two times-table • use known number facts and place value to carry out mentally simple divisions
			Year 4	• develop written methods for TU ÷ U
	Northern Ireland	Number	KS 2	• develop understanding of division and develop range of noncalculator methods of computation
	Republic of Ireland	Number	3rd	• divide a two-digit number by a one-digit number without remainders
			3rd/4th	• develop and recall division facts within 100
	Scotland	Number	B	• divide mentally by two within the confines of this table • divide two-digit numbers by two, without a calculator
	Wales	Number	KS 2	• know multiplication facts and use these to derive the corresponding division facts • develop non-calculator written methods for division
Picture from the Bayeux Tapestry	England	Calculations	Year 4	• derive division facts corresponding to 2, 4 and 5 times-tables • use known number facts and place value to divide integers • develop written methods for TU ÷ U
	Northern Ireland	Number	KS 2	• develop understanding of division and develop range of noncalculator methods of computation
	Republic of Ireland	Number	3rd	• divide a two-digit number by a one-digit number with remainders
			3rd/4th	• develop and recall division facts within 100
	Scotland	Number	B	• divide mentally by 2, 4 and 5 within the confines of these tables • divide two-digit numbers by 2, 4 or 5 without a calculator
	Wales	Number	KS 2	• know multiplication facts and use these to derive the corresponding division facts • develop non-calculator written methods for division
Starry Night	England	Number	Year 3	• recognise unit fractions such as half, third etc.
			Year 3/4	• begin to recognise simple fractions that are several parts of a whole, such as three quarters, two thirds etc.
	Northern Ireland	Number	KS 2	• understand and use fractions
	Republic of Ireland	Number	3rd/4th	• solve and complete practical tasks involving fractions
			4th	• identify fractions with denominators 2, 3, 4, 5, 8 and 10
	Scotland	Number	A	• work with halves
			B	• work with quarters
			C	• work with thirds, fifths, eighths and tenths
	Wales	Number	KS 2	• understand and use fractions to describe proportions of a whole
Down on his Luck	England	Number	Year 4	• begin to relate fractions to division and find simple fractions, such as half, third, quarter, fifth, tenth of numbers
	Northern Ireland	Number	KS 2	• understand and use fractions
	Republic of Ireland	Number	3rd	• develop an understanding of the relationship between fractions and division; for example, quarter of 32 = 8 • calculate a unit fraction of a number; for example, what is quarter of 12?
	Scotland	Number	C	• find simple fractions (third, fifth, tenth) of quantities involving one or two-digit numbers
	Wales	Number	KS 2	• understand and use fractions to describe proportion of a whole

x

Activity	Country	Maths strand	Level	Objective
False Perspective	England	Number	Year 3	• read and write whole numbers to 1000 • know what each digit represents and partition three-digit numbers in HTU
	Northern Ireland	Number	KS 2	• read and write whole numbers to 100 and beyond, understanding that the position of a digit signifies its value
	Republic of Ireland	Number	3rd	• explore and identify place value in whole numbers to 999 • read and write three-digit numbers
	Scotland	Number	B	• work with, and read and write, whole numbers to 1000
	Wales	Number	KS 2	• read and write integers, understanding that the position of a digit signifies its value
Vertumnus	England	Calculations	Year 5	• know by heart all multiplication facts to 10 x 10 • use known number facts and place value to multiply • use written methods to complete long multiplication (TU x TU)
	Northern Ireland	Number	KS 2	• know the multiplication facts to 10 x 10 • develop a range of non-calculator methods of computation for multiplication
	Republic of Ireland	Number	3rd/4th 4th	• develop and recall multiplication facts within 100 • multiply a two-digit number by a two-digit number
	Scotland	Number	C	• multiply mentally within the confines of all tables to 10 • multiply two-digit whole numbers by a whole number with two digits
	Wales	Number	KS 2	• know the multiplication facts to 10 x 10 • use written methods to develop non-calculator methods of multiplication

CURRICULUM LINKS – ART

The activities in *Maths Masterpieces (Middle)* provide the following art opportunities for pupils.

Country	Subject	Strand	Level	Objective
England	Art and Design	Knowledge and Understanding	KS 2	• know about the roles and purposes of artists working in different times and cultures
Northern Ireland	Art and Design	Investigating and Realising	KS 2	• become familiar with a range of art from the past and present and from different cultures
Republic of Ireland	Visual Arts	Looking and Responding	3rd/4th	• look at and talk about the work of artists
Scotland	Art and Design	Evaluating and Appreciating	C D	• research artists • comment upon a wide range of artists' work • use range of resources, including information on artists • evaluate work of others
Wales	Art	Understanding	KS 2	• examine a variety of art from different periods, places and cultures

The activities could also be used as an introduction to a range of art activities, including:

• describing the work of artists

• comparing artists' work to own work and work of other artists

• experimenting with methods used by artists

• researching famous artists

• visiting an art gallery

• developing own ideas and themes using artists as a starting point/reference.

Young Man with Red Hair

Background information

Young Man with Red Hair

by Amadeo Modigliani (1884 –1920)

Modigliani was born in Italy but spent most of his life as a painter in France. He developed his own unique style of painting showing graceful, elongated figures.

He became interested in sculpture but was forced to give this up because the dust from the carved stone affected his lungs (already weakened by tuberculosis).

In spite of the regard he is held in today, Modigliani's life was characterised by extreme poverty. He told friends, 'I am going to drink myself to death'. He succeeded in a short time to fulfil his declaration. His mistress, Jeanne Hebuterne, who was pregnant with their second child, committed suicide the day after his death.

Internet image search

☞ *Jeanne Hebuterne with White Collar*
☞ *Pierrot*
☞ *Head of a Woman with a Hat*
☞ *Bride and Groom*
☞ *Lalotte*
☞ *Madame Zborowska on a Sofa*
☞ *Portrait of Beatrice Hastings*

Pupil instructions

1. Cut out the tiles from the jigsaw sheet.

2. Match the words on the tiles to their words or pictures on the backing board.

3. Glue the tiles onto their matching spaces.

4. Colour the picture in an interesting way.

Talking mathematically

The origins of many of these words are interesting.

'Tri' is a Latin prefix used in many English words associated with three, such as *triangle* (three angles), *trident* (a fork with three prongs – literally three teeth), *tricycle* (three wheels), *triceratops* (three horns). The *try* in Rugby League is so-called because for many years it was counted as three points.

A right angle is the right angle for building. A wall that is not built at 90° to the horizon will not stand as well as one that is.

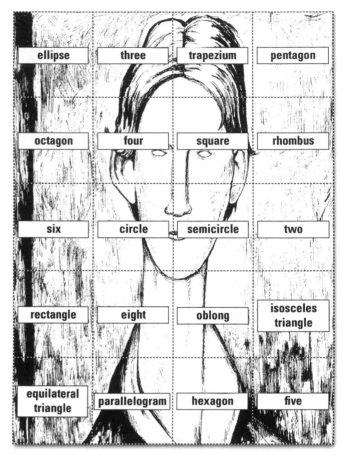

'Quad' is another prefix from Latin and is associated with the number four. Some other *'quad'* words are *quadruped* (an animal with four feet), *quadruple* (multiply by four), *quadruplet* (each of four children born at one birth), *quad* (a motor cycle with four large tyres for off-road use), *quadriplegic* (a person afflicted with paralysis of all four limbs), and *quadrilateral* (any closed figure made up of four straight sides).

The prefix *'oct'* comes from the Ancient Greek word *'ŏkto'* which was also adopted by the Romans. In each case it denotes something to do with the number eight. Octopus comes from the Greek words *'okkto'* (eight) and *'pous'* (foot). The correct plural for this word is *octopodes* or *octopuses*, but not *octopi*.

MATHS MASTERPIECES

Young Man with Red Hair

an oval or ?	a triangle has ____ sides		
	a quadrilateral has ____ sides		
a hexagon has ____ sides			a semicircle has ____ sides
	an octagon has ____ sides	another name for a rectangle is an ?	? triangle
? triangle			a pentagon has ____ sides

Young Man with Red Hair

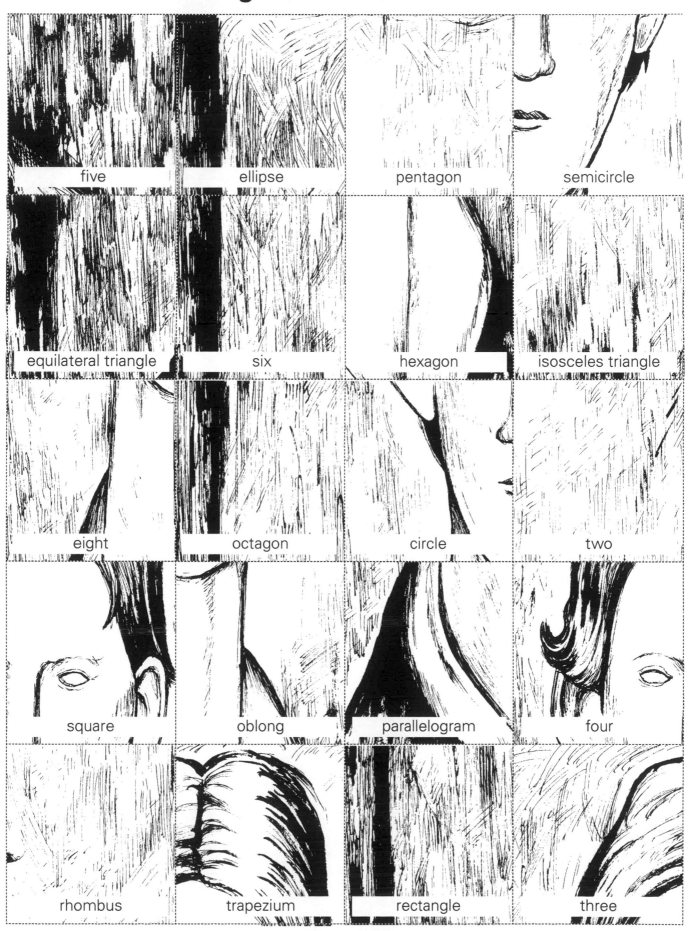

five	ellipse	pentagon	semicircle
equilateral triangle	six	hexagon	isosceles triangle
eight	octagon	circle	two
square	oblong	parallelogram	four
rhombus	trapezium	rectangle	three

Colour Theory

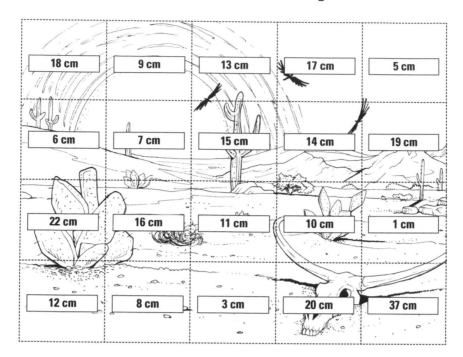

18 cm	9 cm	13 cm	17 cm	5 cm
6 cm	7 cm	15 cm	14 cm	19 cm
22 cm	16 cm	11 cm	10 cm	1 cm
12 cm	8 cm	3 cm	20 cm	37 cm

Background information

Colour theory

Colour can be used to create various impressions in art. Red, yellow, orange (all in various shades) and black are often used to create the impression of warmth. The blues, on the other hand, are considered to be cool colours.

Internet image search

☞ *Sofala* (by Russell Drysdale)

☞ *The Eagle and the Baobab Tree* (by Clifton Pugh)

☞ *Giraffes* (by Sidney Nolan)

☞ *The MacDonnell Ranges* (by Sidney Nolan)

☞ *Trees on a Hillside* (by Fred Williams)

☞ *The Scream* (by Edvard Munch)

Pupil instructions

1. Pupils add the lengths of the lines in centimetres and write the total.

2. Match the tile numbers with the lengths on the puzzle sheet.

3. Glue the tiles on their correct spaces.

Talking mathematically

Pupils may use this method to measure and find the total lengths of shapes made from a number of component lines.

Colour Theory

3.0 cm + 1.5 cm + 0.5 cm	4.5 cm + 4.5 cm + 3.5 cm + 6.5 cm	0.5 cm + 0.5 cm	10.5 cm +15.5 cm +11.0 cm
2.5 cm + 3.5 cm + 2.5 cm + 8.5 cm	5.5 cm + 3.5 cm + 3.5 cm + 1.5 cm	3.5 cm + 2.5 cm + 2.0 cm + 2.0 cm	9.5 cm + 4.5 cm + 2.5 cm + 3.5 cm
6.5 cm + 1.5 cm + 1.5 cm + 3.5 cm	9.5 cm + 5.5 cm	2.5 cm + 5.5 cm + 3.0 cm	1.5 cm + 1.5 cm
3.0 cm + 4.5 cm + 1.5 cm	3.5 cm + 2.5 cm + 1.0 cm	6.5 cm + 5.5 cm + 4.0 cm	1.5 cm + 5.5 cm + 1.0 cm
10.5 cm + 1.5 cm + 6.0 cm	2.5 cm + 1.5 cm + 1.5 cm + 0.5 cm	12.5 cm + 4.5 cm + 4.5 cm + 0.5 cm	6.0 cm + 2.0 cm + 2.5 cm + 1.5 cm

MATHS MASTERPIECES

Colour Theory

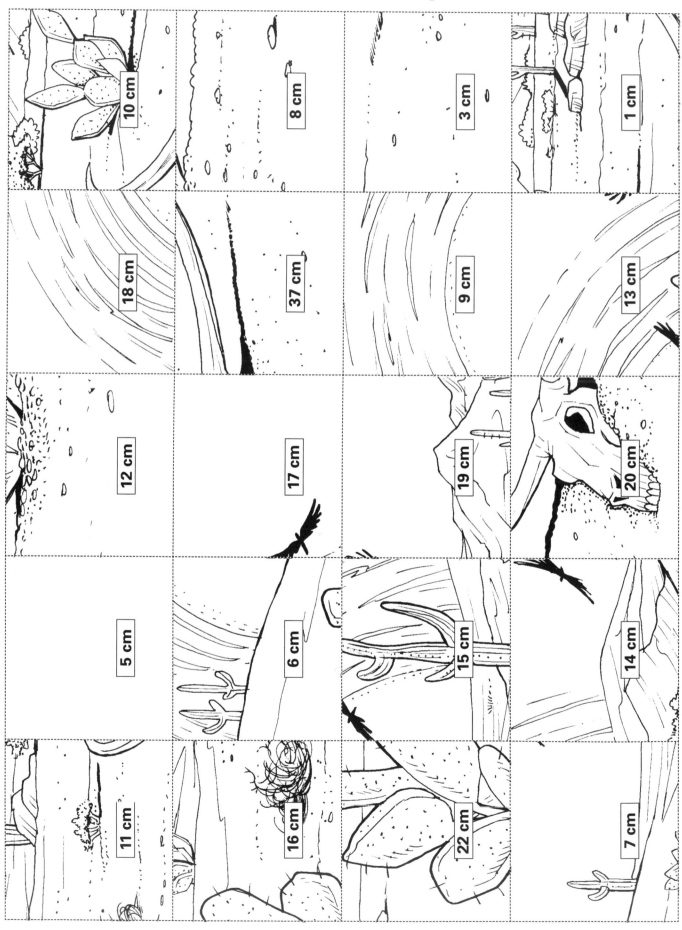

Linear Perspective

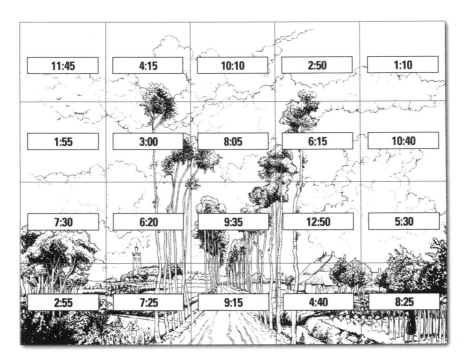

Background information

Linear perspective

by Meindert Hobbema (1638 – 1709)

Perspective is used by artists to give the illusion of depth. Pictures drawn or painted on a flat two-dimensional surface appear to have three dimensions through the use of perspective.

Linear perspective involves the use of lines converging at a central point (called the vanishing point) on the horizon.

Internet image search

☞ *Paris Street: A Rainy Day* (by Gustave Caillebotte)

☞ *Bourke Street* (by Tom Roberts)

☞ *The Last Supper* (by Leonardo da Vinci)

☞ *Annunciation* (by Leonardo da Vinci)

☞ *Golden Gate Bridge* (by Ray Strong)

Pupil instructions

1. Cut out the tiles from the jigsaw sheet.

2. Match each digital time to its analogue clock face on the backing board.

3. Glue the tiles onto their matching spaces.

4. Colour the picture in an interesting way.

Talking mathematically

Pupils can count by fives around the clock face to assist them in becoming familiar with telling the time on an analogue clock. Count to demonstrate 'to' times. For example, when demonstrating 3:40 place a finger on the 8 and count 20, 15, 10 and 5 minutes before the fourth hour. Note that 'to' is only used beyond 'half past' the hour.

Linear Perspective

Linear Perspective

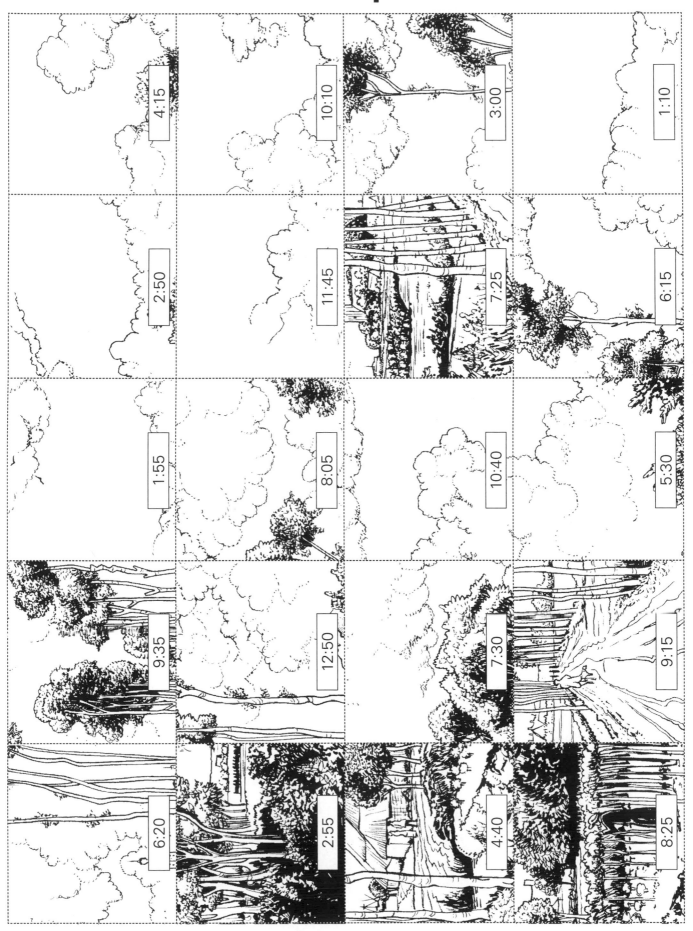

MATHS MASTERPIECES
Still Life with Apples

Background information

Still Life with Apples

by Paul Cezanne (1839 – 1906)

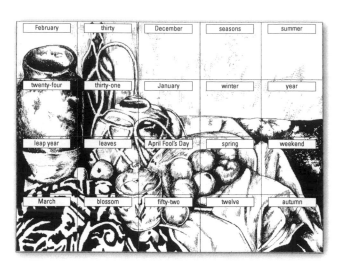

Paul Cezanne was a French artist who experimented with a number of painting styles. He was a leading figure in the art movement known as Impressionism.

Unlike most of the artists who preceded them, Impressionists felt that clarity of detail was not the most important thing in paintings. Impressionists were more interested in the mood created by light and colours in their paintings. So impressionists' paintings do not have a photographic quality about them.

The key subject of the painting does not dominate against a drab background. Rather, impressionist artists concentrate on their impression of a scene—its colours, shades, light and atmosphere.

Cezanne liked to paint outdoors. In 1906 he was caught in a thunderstorm, became ill and died a week later.

Internet image search

☞ *Impression Sunrise (by Claude Monet)*
    (The impressionist movement took its name from this painting)

☞ *Les Baigneurs au Repos (Bathers at Rest)*

☞ *Landscape at Auvers*

☞ *Houses at the Edge of a Road*

☞ *Mont St Victoire*

☞ *The Garden at les Lauves*

☞ *Mont de Cengle*

☞ *Still Life with Watermelon*

Pupil instructions

1. Cut the tiles from jigsaw sheet.

2. Match the words on the tiles to their sentences on the backing board.

3. Glue the tiles onto their matching spaces.

4. Colour the picture in an interesting way.

Talking mathematically

The word *calendar* is linked to the Latin word *kalendarium*, meaning *account book*. This word, however, derives from a word meaning to *call out*. Before there was such a thing as an account book, it was the practice for a herald to proclaim the beginning of each month and upon this declaration all debts became due for collection. As knowledge of the movement of the earth, moon and stars increased and things could be determined in advance, merchants began keeping their own account books (kalendaria). This enabled them to know when debts and interests were due.

The names of the months also derive from Latin and honour important figures, both real and mythological, occasions or, mundanely, their position. March was the first month of the Roman calendar and honoured *Mars*, the Roman god of war. April is believed to had derived from the Latin word *aperie*, meaning *to open*. Being springtime, this was the time for the opening (blossoming) of trees and flowers. May was named after *Maia* (the goddess of increase) who presided over the growth of plants. June is the month of *Juno*, the Roman queen of heaven. July was the birth month of *Julius Caesar*, the great Roman emperor. It is said that Marc Antony, one of Caesar's murderers, named it after the emperor in the same year that he took part in his assassination. Caesar's nephew, Augustus, followed him as emperor and proclaimed the name August to honour himself. September *(the seventh)*, October *(the eighth)*, November *(the ninth)* and December *(the tenth)* are just named according to their position in the Roman calendar. January honours *Janus*, the god of doors and gates. His head has two faces, one which could look back at the past (the old year) and forward (into the new year). February takes its name from the Latin word *februare* meaning to *cleanse*. This was the month in which a *cleansing* festival was held. A feature of this month was the *cleansing* of women who were infertile. They were beaten with thonged goatskins cut from the hides of two goats who were sacrificed as part of the ceremonies. This was meant to purify the women so they would be able, thereafter, to bear children.

When the calendar (known as the Julian calendar after Julius Caesar) was revised in 1582 (to the Gregorian calendar after Pope Gregory XIII) the seventh, eighth, ninth and tenth months retained their titles even though their positions were now changed.

Still Life with Apples

June and July are months in the season of ☐☐☐☐☐☐ .

There are 365 days in a ☐☐☐☐ .

Saturday and Sunday make up the ☐☐☐☐☐☐☐ .

September and October are months in the season of ☐☐☐☐☐☐ .

Spring, summer, autumn and winter are the ☐☐☐☐☐☐☐ .

December and January are months in the season of ☐☐☐☐☐☐ .

March and April are months in the season of ☐☐☐☐☐ .

There are ☐☐☐☐☐ months in a year.

Christmas is in the month of ☐☐☐☐☐☐☐☐ .

New Year's Day is on the first of ☐☐☐☐☐☐☐ .

The first of April is called ☐☐☐☐☐' ☐☐☐ .

A year is made up of ☐☐ – ☐☐ weeks.

September, April, June and November all have ☐☐ days.

January, March, May, July, August, October and December all have ☐☐ – ☐☐ days.

Some trees lose their ☐☐☐☐☐☐ in autumn.

Many trees ☐☐☐☐☐☐ in spring.

The shortest month is ☐☐☐☐☐☐☐☐ .

A day has ☐☐ – ☐☐ hours.

There are 366 days in a ☐☐☐☐ .

The third month is ☐☐☐☐☐ .

MATHS MASTERPIECES

Still Life with Apples

January

winter

year

April Fool's Day

leaves

weekend

spring

autumn

twenty-four

twelve

fifty-two

blossom

February

March

seasons

thirty-one

December

thirty

leap year

summer

Jonah and the Whale

Background information

Jonah and the Whale

by Ambrogio Bondone Giotto (1266 – 1337)

Giotto lived in Italy. He was a farmer's son who was discovered drawing sheep by the famous artist, Giovanni Cimabue. Cimabue offered to tutor Giotto but the student's fame grew to the extent that he overshadowed his master.

The painting of Jonah and the whale is part of a fresco on the walls of the Arena Chapel in the Italian city of Padua. A fresco is a painting done quickly on wet plaster so that the colours penetrate the plaster and become fixed when it dries.

A story is told concerning Giotto and Pope Benedict IX. The pope was interested in employing Giotto and sent a messenger to take back an example of his work. When asked this, Giotto dipped his paintbrush in some red paint and with a single sweep of his hand painted a perfect circle.

Internet image search

☞ *St Francis Preaching to the Birds*

☞ *Madonna and Child*

☞ *The Mourning of Christ*

☞ *Expulsion of Joachim from the Temple*

☞ *The Visitation*

☞ *Crucifixion*

☞ *Homage of a Simple Man*

☞ *Christ's Ascension*

Pupil instructions

1. Cut out the tiles from the jigsaw sheet.

2. Do the addition sums on the backing board.

3. Match the numbers on the tiles to the answers on the backing board.

4. Glue the tiles onto their matching spaces.

5. Colour the picture in an interesting way.

Talking mathematically

It is important that the pupils understand our number system and the importance of place value when doing these sums. Sums allow us to calculate amounts quickly and efficiently. For example, to combine a group of 30 with a group of 33 (as in the sum 30+33) without a sum, it would be necessary to first draw 30 things, like this:

* * * * * * x x *

and then draw 33 things like this:

* *

and then combine them into a single group like this:

* *
* *

MATHS MASTERPIECES

Jonah and the Whale

12 + 11	22 + 21	23 + 32	30 + 33
15 + 14	30 + 10	17 + 21	24 + 32
12 + 14	12 + 20	33 + 32	16 + 21
34 + 41	21 + 40	25 + 24	34 + 32
34 + 42	43 + 42	32 + 22	32 + 32

Jonah and the Whale

MATHS MASTERPIECES

Monarch of the Glen

Background information

Monarch of the Glen
by Sir Edward Landseer (1802 – 1873)

Landseer was an Englishman who was to become Queen Victoria's favourite artist. He showed talent at a very early age and had an exhibition of his drawings at London's Royal Academy when he was only 13 years old. Landseer's subjects were mostly animals but he tried to portray them showing various human expressions. The stag in his most famous painting, *Monarch of the Glen*, looks proud and noble.

Landseer's paintings lost favour in the twentieth century because some people were concerned that some of them seemed to emphasise deer hunting.

Internet image search

☞ *Deer and Deerhounds in a Mountain Torrent*

☞ *Dignity and Impudence*

☞ *Marmosets on a Pineapple*

☞ *Laying Down the Law*

☞ *Flood in the Highlands*

☞ *The Old Shepherd's Chief Mourner*

☞ *Collie Rescuing a Sheep*

☞ *Man Proposes – God Disposes*

Additional activity

Find and write the dictionary meanings of the words 'dignity' and 'impudence'. Explain why Landseer may have chosen to use these words in the title of his painting *Dignity and Impudence*.

Pupil instructions

1. Cut out the tiles from the jigsaw sheet.

2. Do the addition sums on the backing board.

3. Match the numbers on the tiles to the answers on the backing board.

4. Glue the tiles onto their matching spaces.

5. Colour the picture in an interesting way.

Talking mathematically

To understand trading, pupils need a sound understanding of place value in the Hindu-Arabic number system. Memory joggers can be used to help. In the first example (15 + 37), when adding the units column (7 + 5) and getting the answer 12, you might suggest that the pupils write the two ones in the units column (together with the other 'one-year-olds') and carry the big '10-year-old' up with the other big 10-year-olds (the 10s column). This is a method that seems to strike a chord with some children.

There is, of course, an abundance of materials and explanations that can be used to instill this understanding.

Monarch of the Glen

15 + 37	16 + 17	48 + 46	18 + 17
27 + 37	29 + 36	44 + 36	29 + 45
35 + 18	23 + 37	19 + 73	65 + 16
18 + 14	27 + 34	19 + 29	29 + 38
59 + 34	73 + 18	58 + 39	26 + 56

MATHS MASTERPIECES

Monarch of the Glen

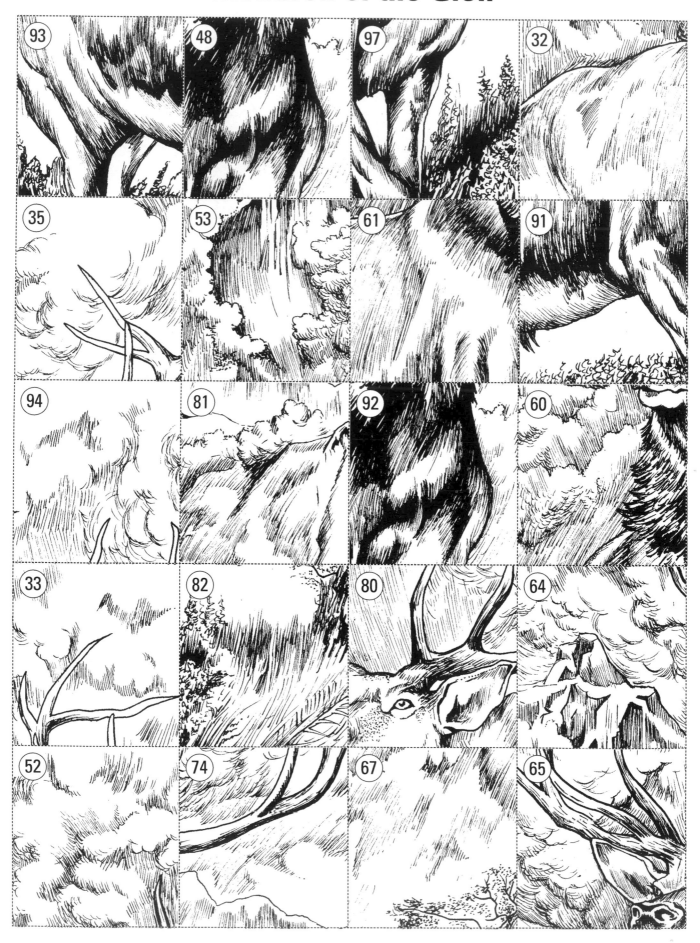

Maths masterpieces

Ancient Cave Painting

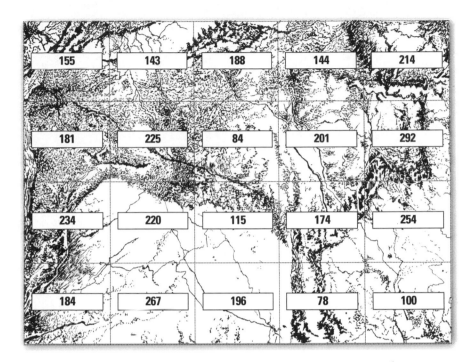

Background information

Ancient Cave Painting

The cave painting of a bison was painted on a cave wall at Altamira in Spain over 20 000 years ago. Firstly, the artist scratched an outline using something hard such as flint. After this, the colour was filled in using natural materials such as ground-up minerals. The chief colours of the original painting are brown, red and yellow.

Internet image search

☞ *Lascaux Cave*

☞ *Altamira Cave*

Pupil instructions

1. Cut out the tiles from the jigsaw sheet.

2. Do the addition sums on the backing board.

3. Match the numbers on the tiles to the answers on the backing board.

4. Glue the tiles onto their matching spaces.

5. Colour the picture in an interesting way.

Talking mathematically

There is, of course, an abundance of materials and explanations that can be used to instill this understanding.

Pupils who have not fully understood trading will often carry the wrong numbers up to the 10s column. They often become used to carrying one without understanding that it is the number in the units column of the answer that is written. In these examples, pupils must write both numbers in their answer if the tens column adds to more than nine. Pupils should have this explained to them before attempting the activity, if they are not already well-practised in this type of sum.

MATHS MASTERPIECES

Ancient Cave Painting

68 64 + 82	97 96 + 99	98 89 + 67	18 66 + 16
49 48 + 47	53 97 + 51	83 87 + 4	33 32 + 13
67 37 + 84	38 17 + 29	88 13 + 14	64 66 + 66
76 18 + 49	65 75 + 85	70 74 + 76	95 95 + 77
32 48 + 75	97 63 + 21	99 99 + 36	63 36 + 85

Ancient Cave Painting

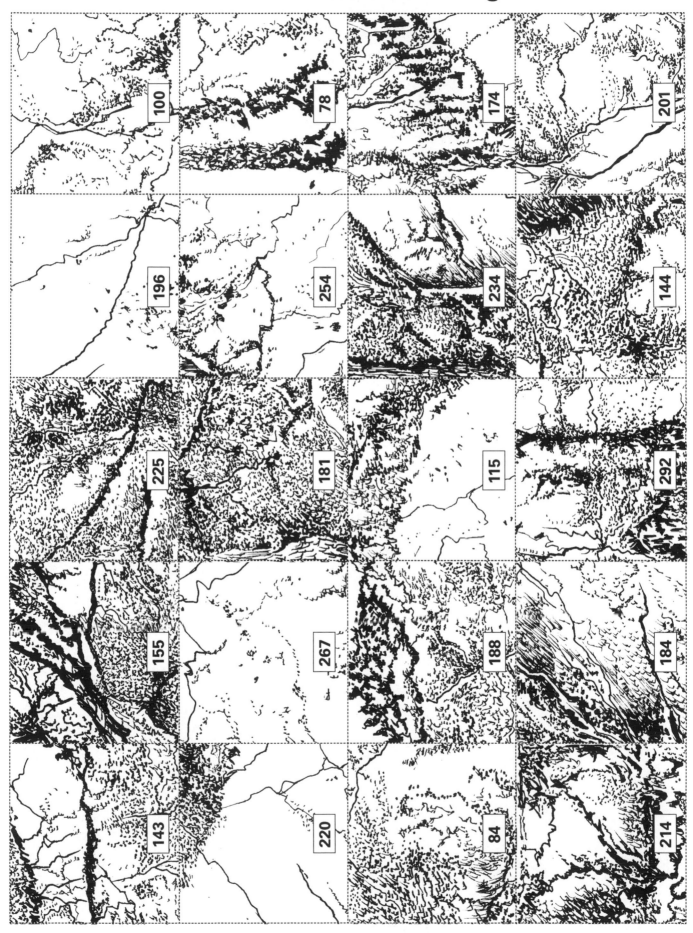

Teachers notes

The Haywain

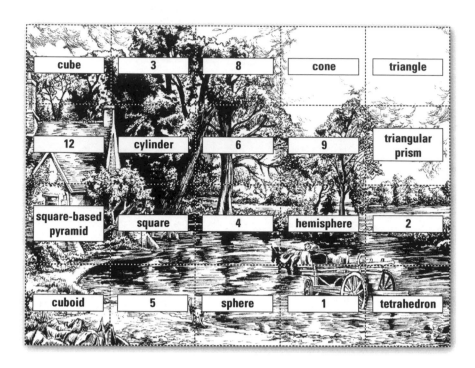

cube	3	8	cone	triangle
12	cylinder	6	9	triangular prism
square-based pyramid	square	4	hemisphere	2
cuboid	5	sphere	1	tetrahedron

Background information

The Haywain

by John Constable (1776 – 1837)

John Constable was the son of a wealthy merchant and mill owner. Constable loved the countryside, particularly that of his native area of Suffolk in England. Nature always features in his paintings. Clouds, too, are an important part of most of his paintings. *The Haywain* ('wain' is an old word meaning 'cart') was awarded a gold medal by the French Emperor, Charles X.

Internet image search

☞ *Dedham Church and Vale*

☞ *His Majesty's Ship 'Victory'*

☞ *Landscape: Boys Fishing*

☞ *Boat Building*

☞ *Flatford Mill*

Pupil instructions

1. Cut out the tiles from the jigsaw sheet.

2. Match the numbers and words on the tiles to the answers on the backing board.

3. Glue the tiles onto their matching spaces.

4. Colour the picture in an interesting way.

Talking mathematically

Pupils should know that 3–D shapes have faces (each face is a flat surface and a 2–D shape), edges (the line where two faces meet) and vertices (the points where three or more edges meet).

There are patterns in the properties of 3–D shapes; for example,

Pyramids:

• have an even number of edges

• have the same number of faces and vertices

• have one more face than the number of edges on the base.

The Haywain

What shape are the faces on a tetrahedron? ____		A cone has ____ faces.	
	A triangular prism has ____ edges.		A hemisphere has ____ edge.
A square-based pyramid has ____ edges.	A cuboid has ____ faces.	A tetrahedron has ____ vertices.	
A cylinder has ____ faces.		What shape are the faces on a cube? ____	A triangular prism has ____ faces.
	A cube has ____ edges.		

MATHS MASTERPIECES

The Haywain

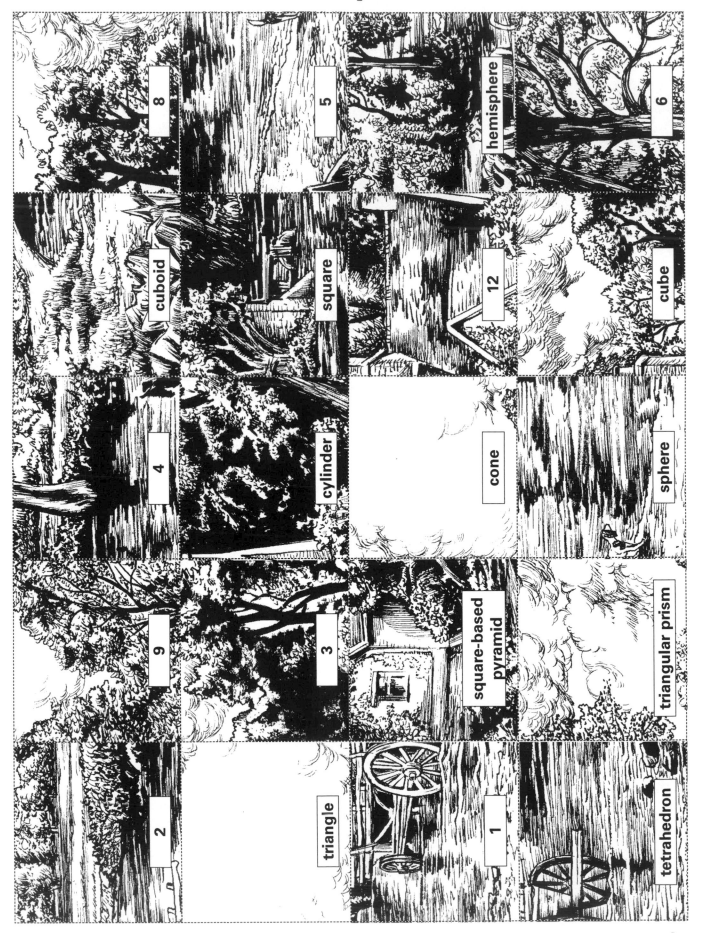

Henry VIII

Background information

Henry VIII of England

by Hans Holbein (1497 - 1543)

Holbein was a German painter who moved to England in 1526. He painted portraits of wealthy and powerful people and came to the notice of King Henry VIII, who made him his court painter. When Henry was looking for a new wife (he was married six times) he asked Holbein to travel overseas and paint portraits of likely women. Henry fell in love with Holbein's portrait of Anne of Cleves and married her. Holbein died of bubonic plague in London in 1543.

Internet image search

- ☞ *Sir Richard Southwell*
- ☞ *Dorothea Kannengiesser*
- ☞ *Adam & Eve*
- ☞ *The Body of the Dead Christ in the Tomb*
- ☞ *Sir Thomas More*
- ☞ *The Artist's Family*

Pupil instructions

1. Cut out the tiles from the jigsaw sheet.
2. Do the subtraction sums on the backing board.
3. Match the numbers on the tiles to the answers on the backing board.
4. Glue the tiles onto their matching spaces.
5. Colour the picture in an interesting way.

Talking mathematically

It is important to remind the pupils that they must always start with the smallest column (i.e. the units column). This becomes more important when examples involve trading. On the other hand, if a pupil discovers that the order of column subtraction does not matter in these examples, commend him/her on being thoughtful and investigative.

MATHS MASTERPIECES

Henry VIII

50 − 30	69 − 40	84 − 43	75 − 22
67 − 54	87 − 44	98 − 31	99 − 63
58 − 46	79 − 55	87 − 43	68 − 41
96 − 42	97 − 26	66 − 35	88 − 33
96 − 24	79 − 41	89 − 54	68 − 16

Henry VIII

Teachers notes

The Sleep of Reason Produces Monsters

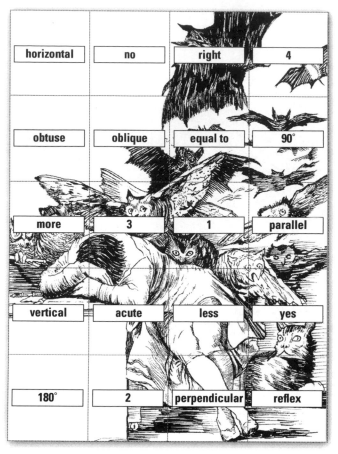

horizontal	no	right	4
obtuse	oblique	equal to	90°
more	3	1	parallel
vertical	acute	less	yes
180°	2	perpendicular	reflex

Background information

The Sleep of Reason Produces Monsters
by Francisco Goya (1746 – 1828)

The Sleep of Reason Produces Monsters is a self-portrait of the artist at a difficult time in his life. He was stricken by a lengthy illness between 1792 and 1793, leaving him deaf. Goya was Spanish and a very influential painter. He is famous for depicting the horrors of war in a series of paintings showing scenes from Napoleon's invasion and occupation of Spain (1808 – 1814).

Internet image search

- ☞ *The Esquilache Riots*
- ☞ *The Sacrifice to Vesta*
- ☞ *The Kite*
- ☞ *Fight at the Cock Inn*
- ☞ *The Parasol*
- ☞ *The Snowstorm*

Pupil instructions

1. Cut out the tiles from the jigsaw sheet.
2. Match the numbers and words on the tiles to the answers on the backing board.
3. Glue the tiles onto their matching spaces.
4. Colour the picture in an interesting way.

Talking mathematically

Pupils should investigate lines of symmetry in regular 2–D shapes. They should conclude that the number of lines of symmetry in a regular 2–D shape is equal to the number of sides; for example, an equilateral triangle has three lines of symmetry, a square four and a regular hexagon six.

Pupils should know and understand the definitions of different lines; for example, horizontal, vertical, perpendicular, oblique and parallel. They should be able to recognise the lines in 2–D shapes and the environment.

Initially, pupils should know that an acute angle is less than a right angle and an obtuse angle is greater than a right angle. As pupils become proficient with the use of a protractor they should know that:

right angle = 90°

acute angle = less than 90°

straight line = 180°

obtuse angle = between 90° and 180°

reflex angle = between 180° and 360°.

The Sleep of Reason Produces Monsters

a ___?___ line	Are the angles in an equilateral triangle all right angles?	a ___?___ angle	How many lines of symmetry in a square?
an ___?___ angle	an ___?___ line	Are the angles in a square *less than* or *equal to* right angles?	How many degrees in a right angle?
Are the angles in a hexagon *less* than or *more* than right angles?	How many lines of symmetry in an equilateral triangle?	How many lines of symmetry in a semicircle?	___?___ lines
a ___?___ line	an ___?___ angle	Are the angles in an equilateral triangle *less* than or *greater* than right angles?	Are the angles in a rectangle all right angles?
How many degrees in a straight angle (or two right angles)?	How many lines of symmetry in a rectangle?	a ___?___ line	a ___?___ angle

MATHS MASTERPIECES

The Sleep of Reason Produces Monsters

2   equal to   vertical   3

reflex   perpendicular   more   yes

oblique   180°   1   less

4   horizontal   obtuse   acute

no   90°   right   parallel

The Milkmaid

Background information

The Milkmaid

by Johannes Vermeer (1632 –1675)

Vermeer was born and lived all of his life in the Dutch town of Delft. Many of his paintings show people doing everyday tasks inside, just as his milkmaid is doing.

Vermeer had 11 children and only produced a small number of paintings each year (only 35 known works exist). When he died unexpectedly at the age of 43 he was heavily in debt.

Internet image search

- ☞ *The Love Letter*
- ☞ *Christ in the House of Mary and Martha*
- ☞ *Diana and her Companions*
- ☞ *Girl Asleep at a Table*
- ☞ *The Glass of Wine*
- ☞ *The Music Lesson*
- ☞ *The Geographer*
- ☞ *The Astronomer*

Pupil instructions

1. Cut out the tiles from the jigsaw sheet.
2. Do the subtraction sums on the backing board.
3. Match the numbers on the tiles to the answers on the backing board.
4. Glue the tiles onto their matching spaces.
4. Colour the picture in an interesting way.

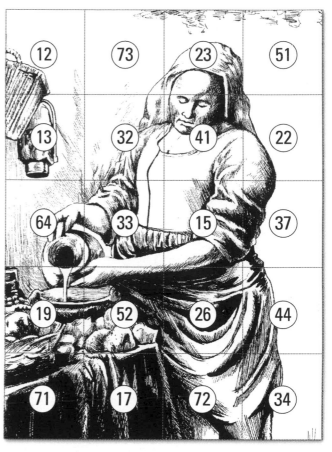

Talking mathematically

Just as with the equal addition of 10s (borrowing and paying back), there is a clear way of explaining what is going on for the equal subtraction of 10s.

For example, for 31 – 19, show 31 as three groups of 10 and one (unit).

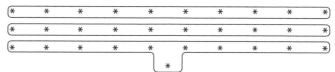

Draw boundary ropes around each bundle of 10.

Ask the pupils:
Have I added any objects? (No)
Have I taken any objects away? (No)

What I have done is to organise the objects differently. (Instead of three bundles of 10 and a single one, I have organised them into two bundles of 10 and 11 ones.)

The Milkmaid

31 − 19	90 − 17	42 − 19	70 − 19
61 − 48	71 − 39	60 − 19	71 − 49
80 − 16	72 − 39	70 − 55	74 − 37
51 − 32	80 − 28	52 − 26	81 − 37
90 − 19	34 − 17	91 − 19	50 − 16

The Milkmaid

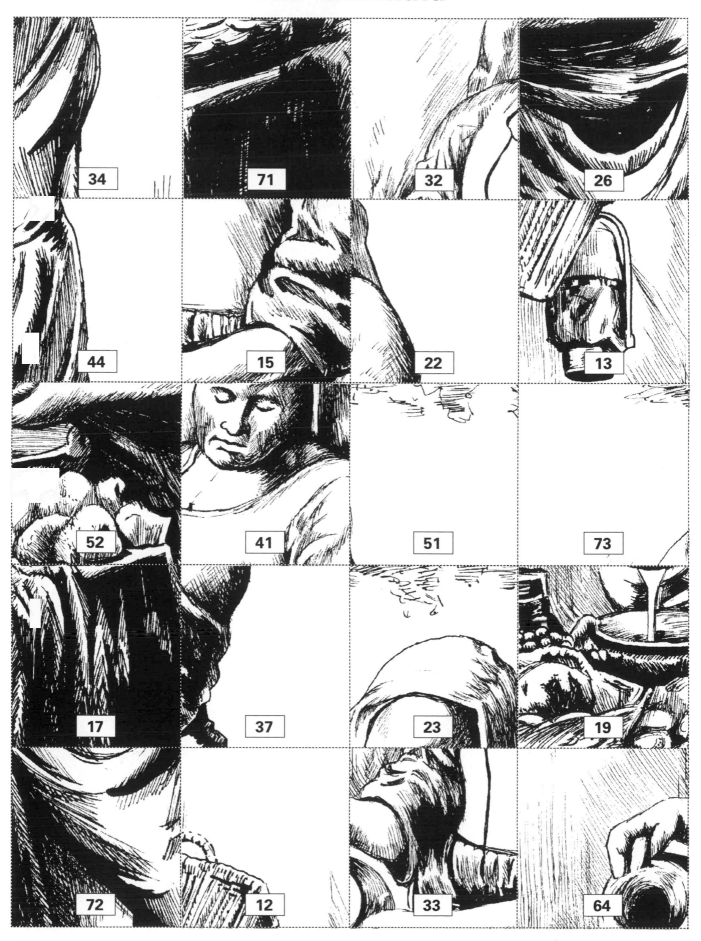

Bubbles

Background information

Bubbles

by Sir John Everett Millais (1829 - 1896)

Millais was an Englishman. At the age of 11 he was the youngest artist ever to join the Royal Academy, Britain's finest art school. He paid great attention to detail in his paintings and background landscapes were painted from nature. Millais and his wife had eight children. His paintings were very popular and sold at high prices during his lifetime. Bubbles is a painting of his grandson, Willie. It was used by a soap company in an advertisement for its product.

Internet image search

- ☞ *The Bridesmaid*
- ☞ *The Return of the Dove to the Ark*
- ☞ *The Blind Girl*
- ☞ *Apple Blossoms*
- ☞ *The Boyhood of Raleigh*

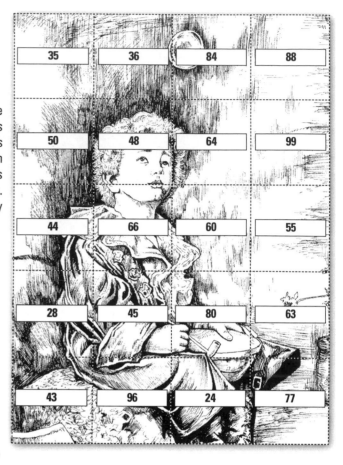

Pupil instructions

1. Cut out the tiles from the jigsaw sheet.

2. Do the multiplication sums on the backing board.

3. Match the number on the tiles to the answers on the backing board.

4. Glue the tiles onto their matching spaces.

5. Colour the picture in an interesting way.

Talking mathematically

It is important to understand why we use sums. In general it has to do with efficiency. By writing a few 'squiggles' (numerals) and applying a sum correctly we can calculate large amounts which would take a great deal of time and effort to calculate by counting.

Multiplication is a shortened method of addition of equal amounts.

Using the sum

$$\begin{array}{r} 3213 \\ \times\ 3 \\ \hline \\ \hline \end{array}$$

as an example, ask pupils how an answer could be found without using a sum.

To count three groups of 3213 would take a great deal of time and effort and is more likely to be inaccurate due to factors such as losing count, being interrupted etc.

As an addition sum, an answer can be achieved by writing 12 numerals and ruling two lines.

$$\begin{array}{r} 3213 \\ 3213 \\ +\ 3213 \\ \hline \end{array}$$

Using a multiplication sum, we can shorten this to five numerals and two lines.

$$\begin{array}{r} 3213 \\ \times\ 3 \\ \hline \end{array}$$

Bubbles

35 x 1	12 x 3	42 x 2	22 x 4
50 x 1	12 x 4	32 x 2	33 x 3
11 x 4	33 x 2	20 x 3	11 x 5
14 x 2	45 x 1	20 x 4	21 x 3
43 x 1	32 x 3	12 x 2	77 x 1

MATHS MASTERPIECES

Bubbles

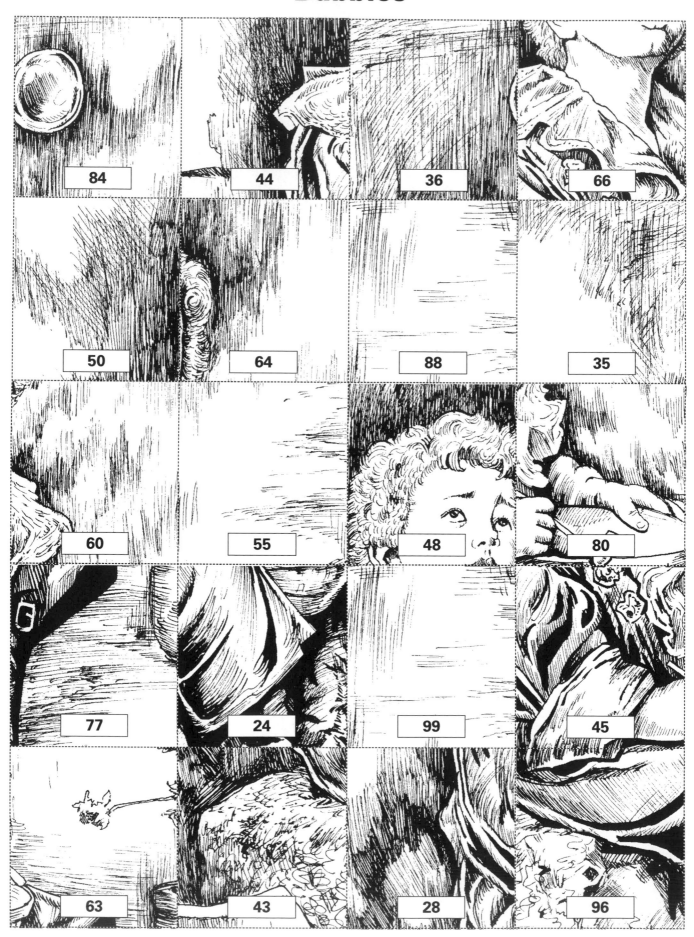

Blue Horses

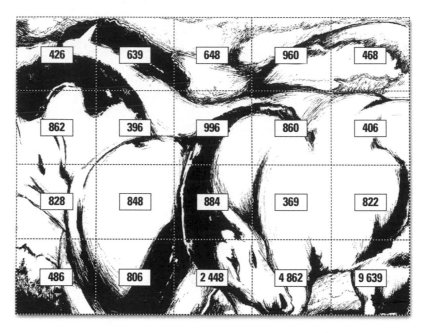

Background information

Blue Horses

by Franz Marc (1880 – 1916)

Franz Marc was a German painter who preferred to paint animals because he felt they lived in true harmony with nature. Marc was influenced by the art movement known as expressionism. Expressionist painters emphasise emotions rather than realism in their paintings. A compelling example of an expressionist painting is Edvard Munch's *The Scream*. Although not a realistic representation of a person, the emotion of terror is clearly conveyed.

Marc was made to join the German army during WWI. He was killed in action at Verdun in France in 1916.

Internet image search

☞ *Bewitched Mill*

☞ *Indersdorf*

☞ *Two Cats, Blue and Yellow*

☞ *Three Cats*

☞ *The Tiger*

☞ *Foxes*

Pupil instructions

1. Cut out the tiles from the jigsaw sheet.

2. Do the multiplication sums on the backing board.

3. Match the numbers on the tiles to the answers on the backing board.

4. Glue the tiles onto their matching spaces.

5. Colour the picture in an interesting way.

Talking mathematically

It is important to understand why we use sums. In general it has to do with efficiency. By writing a few 'squiggles' (numerals) and applying a sum correctly we can calculate large amounts which would take a great deal of time and effort to calculate by counting.

Multiplication is a shortened method of addition of equal amounts.

Using the sum

$$\begin{array}{r} 3213 \\ \times\ 3 \\ \hline \end{array}$$

as an example, ask pupils how an answer could be found without using a sum.

To count three groups of 3213 would take a great deal of time and effort and is more likely to be inaccurate due to factors such as losing count, being interrupted etc.

As an addition sum, an answer can be achieved by writing 12 numerals and ruling two lines.

$$\begin{array}{r} 3213 \\ 3213 \\ +\ 3213 \\ \hline \\ \hline \end{array}$$

Using a multiplication sum, we can shorten this to five numerals and two lines.

$$\begin{array}{r} 3213 \\ \times\ 3 \\ \hline \\ \hline \end{array}$$

Blue Horses

234 × 2 ___	203 × 2 ___	411 × 2 ___	3 213 × 3 ___
320 × 3 ___	430 × 2 ___	123 × 3 ___	2 431 × 2 ___
324 × 2 ___	332 × 3 ___	442 × 2 ___	1 224 × 2 ___
213 × 3 ___	132 × 3 ___	424 × 2 ___	403 × 2 ___
213 × 2 ___	431 × 2 ___	414 × 2 ___	243 × 2 ___

Blue Horses

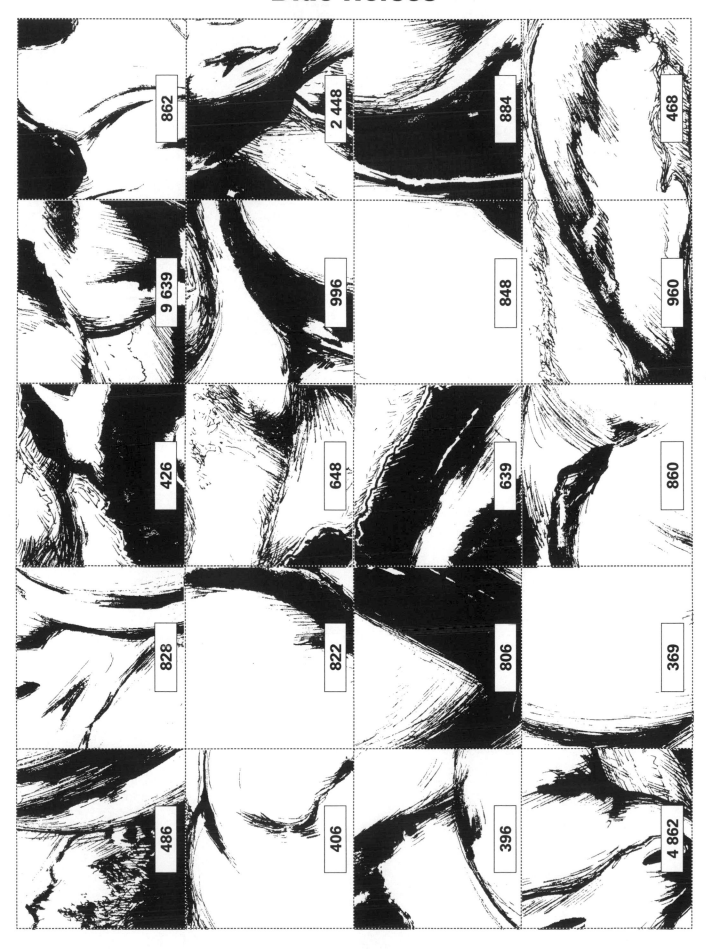

MULTIPLICATION WITH TRADING

Teachers notes

MATHS MASTERPIECES

The Gulf Stream

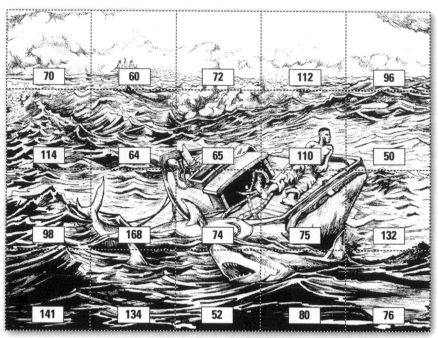

Background information

The Gulf Stream

by Winslow Homer (1836 - 1910)

Homer was an American painter who lived at various times in France, England, Bermuda and the Bahamas. He worked as an illustrator and war artist for the magazine *Harper's Weekly* during the American Civil War. Many of his paintings are on the theme of people setting themselves against nature. In *The Gulf Stream* we see the man in a schooner whose mast has been snapped. A waterspout is approaching and the shark-infested water offers no escape.

Internet image search

☞ *Snap the Whip*

☞ *Eight Bells*

☞ *The Sharpshooter*

☞ *The Herring Net*

☞ *The Fog Warning*

☞ *Right and Left*

☞ *Sponge Fishermen*

☞ *The Bridle Path*

☞ *Kissing the Moon*

Additional activities

Discuss the questions:

• Which of these pictures was an illustration?

• What are the children doing in *Snap the Whip*?

• Why do you think the painting has this name?

Pupil instructions

1. Cut out the tiles from the jigsaw sheet.

2. Do the multiplication sums on the backing board.

3. Match the numbers on the tiles to the answers on the backing board.

4. Glue the tiles onto their matching spaces.

5. Colour the picture in an interesting way.

Talking mathematically

Demonstrate how repeated addition of equal amounts mimics the processes involved in multiplication with trading.

$$\begin{array}{r} 16 \\ \times\,5 \\ \hline 80 \end{array}$$

can also be calculated using the sum

$$\begin{array}{r} 3 \\ +\,16 \\ +\,16 \\ +\,16 \\ +\,16 \\ +\,16 \\ \hline 80 \end{array}$$

The total of the units column can be calculated by adding 6 five times

i.e. 6 + 6 + 6 + 6 + 6 = 30.

Another way of saying this is five lots of 6. Using the addition sum we write down the zero and 'carry' the 3 to the 10s column (to be added later). Using the multiplication sum we write down the zero and 'carry' the 3 to the 10s column (also to be added later). To conclude the addition sum, we add five lots of one and then add the amount carried.

The Gulf Stream

48 × 2	25 × 2	66 × 2	38 × 2
56 × 2	55 × 2	15 × 5	16 × 5
36 × 2	13 × 5	37 × 2	26 × 2
15 × 4	16 × 4	56 × 3	67 × 2
35 × 2	57 × 2	49 × 2	47 × 3

MATHS MASTERPIECES

The Gulf Stream

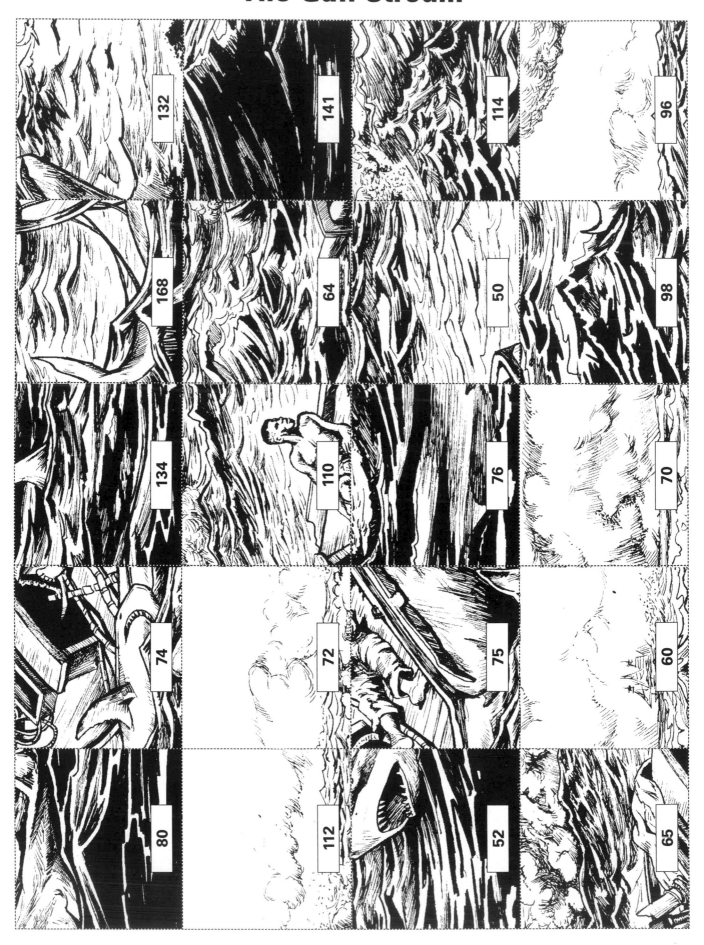

The Laughing Cavalier

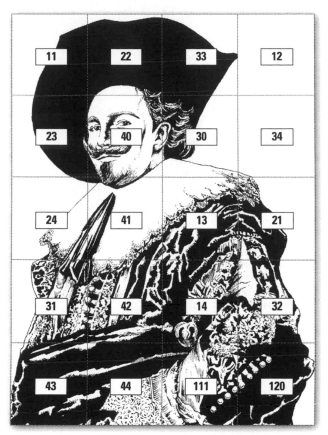

Background information

The Laughing Cavalier

by Frans Hals (1580 - 1666)

Hals was a Dutch portrait painter who was able to capture the character of his subjects more than any artist before his time. Despite his great skill and the popularity of his work, he was penniless when he died.

Internet image search

☞ *The Governors of the Old Men's Almhouse at Haarlem*

☞ *Boy with a Flute*

☞ *Jester with a Lute*

Pupil instructions

1. Cut out the tiles from the jigsaw sheet.

2. Do the division sums on the backing board.

3. Match the numbers on the tiles to the answers on the backing board.

4. Glue the tiles onto their matching spaces.

5. Colour the picture in an interesting way.

Talking mathematically

Various approaches can be used to demonstrate division. For example, 26 'divided by/shared between' 2 can be demonstrated by sharing 26 items between 2 pupils.

Draw 26 'sticks of chalk'.

As you give one each to 'Bruce' and 'Raelene' (or whomever you choose), circle and label these on your diagram. For example:

ⒾB ⒾR ⒾR ⒾR ⒾB ⒾR ⒾB ⒾR ⒾB ⒾR ⒾB ⒾR

ⒾB ⒾR ⒾB ⒾR ⒾB ⒾR ⒾB ⒾR ⒾB ⒾR ⒾB

ⒾR ⒾB ⒾR

Recipient of each piece *(B = Bruce, R = Raelene in this example)*

Ask each pupil how many pieces of chalk they have.

Ask pupils how many times B was written (for Bruce) and how many times R was written (for Raelene).

Using the short division sum $2\overline{)26}$, you are individually calculating 'How many groups of 10 will each child get if they share two groups of 10?' and 'How many ones will each child get if they share six ones?'

The Laughing Cavalier

$2\overline{)22}$	$2\overline{)44}$	$2\overline{)66}$	$2\overline{)24}$
$2\overline{)46}$	$2\overline{)80}$	$2\overline{)60}$	$2\overline{)68}$
$2\overline{)48}$	$2\overline{)82}$	$2\overline{)26}$	$2\overline{)42}$
$2\overline{)62}$	$2\overline{)84}$	$2\overline{)28}$	$2\overline{)64}$
$2\overline{)86}$	$2\overline{)88}$	$2\overline{)222}$	$2\overline{)240}$

The Laughing Cavalier

Teachers notes

Picture from the Bayeux Tapestry

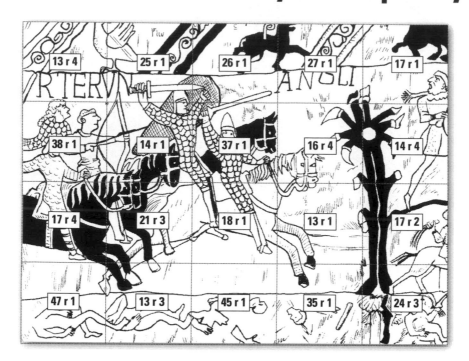

Background information

Picture from the Bayeux Tapestry

The Bayeux Tapestry is an embroidered cloth about 70 metres long and half a metre wide. It illustrates events leading up to and including the Battle of Hastings in 1066. It was this battle between the Norman army led by William the Conqueror and the Saxons led by Harold, Earl of Wessex, that ensured the success of the Norman invasion of England. It took eleven years (from 1066 to 1077) to make the tapestry. It is not really known who made the tapestry. Some historians credit Matilda, William's wife, with making it. Others believe it was stitched by Englishmen from Canterbury.

Internet image search

☞ *Bayeux Tapestry*

Pupil instructions

1. Cut out the tiles from the jigsaw sheet.

2. Do the division sums on the backing board.

3. Match the numbers on the tiles to the answers on the backing board.

4. Glue the tiles onto their matching spaces.

5. Colour the picture in an interesting way.

Talking mathematically

To assist with these sums initially, diagrammatic 'crutches' may be provided to assist pupils with their calculations. For example:

$$4\overline{)99}$$

Diagram: tens / / / / / / / / / ones / / / / / / / / /

Use the diagram to demonstrate nine (10s) divided by 4 (circle two groups of 4).

This leaves one group of 10 and nine ones (19).

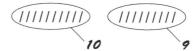

Divide 19 by 4 (circle 4 groups of 4).

Three things 'remain' left over.

We call these the 'remainder'.

Picture from the Bayeux Tapestry

$2\overline{)35}$	$5\overline{)74}$	$5\overline{)87}$	$4\overline{)99}$
$2\overline{)55}$	$5\overline{)84}$	$4\overline{)53}$	$2\overline{)71}$
$2\overline{)53}$	$2\overline{)75}$	$2\overline{)37}$	$2\overline{)91}$
$2\overline{)51}$	$4\overline{)57}$	$4\overline{)87}$	$4\overline{)55}$
$5\overline{)69}$	$2\overline{)77}$	$5\overline{)89}$	$2\overline{)95}$

MATHS MASTERPIECES

Picture from the Bayeux Tapestry

Starry Night

Background information

Starry Night

by Vincent Van Gogh (1853 – 1890)

Vincent Van Gogh was a brilliant artist but led an unsettled life because of recurring periods of mental disturbance. He only began painting at the age of 27, but in the ten-year period of activity before he shot and killed himself, he completed 1 600 paintings.

He was not recognised until after his death and most of his life was lived in abject poverty. He was a friend of the French artist, Paul Gauguin, and it was after an argument with him that Van Gogh cut off part of his own ear. Most of his paintings are made up of separate unblended brush marks. This techniques is clearly seen in *Starry Night*.

Van Gogh always signed his pictures with his first name, Vincent, only.

Internet image search

☞ *Sunflowers*

☞ *Seashore at Scheveningen*

Pupil instructions

1. Cut out the tiles from the jigsaw sheet.

2. Write the fraction indicated by the shading on each shape on the backing board.

3. Match the fractions on the tiles to the fractions on the backing board.

4. Glue the tiles onto their matching spaces.

5. Colour the picture in an interesting way.

Talking mathematically

It is important that pupils clearly understand what the numerator and denominator of a fraction stand for. Pupils can often tell you the names numerator and denominator but are not always clear on their meaning.

The **denominator** (bottom number) tells us the number of equal sized parts a shape is divided (cut etc.) into.

The **numerator** is the number of these parts that we are considering (talking about).

Draw a shape similar to the one shown and ask pupils, *'What fraction of this cake has icing (is shaded)?'*

To find the answers, follow these steps.

Step 1 – *Draw the fraction bar (line separating numerator and denominator).*

Step 2 – *The denominator (bottom number) tells us the number of equal sized parts a shape is divided (cut etc.) into. This cake is divided into 5 equal sized pieces so the bottom number is 5.*

Step 3 – *The numerator is the number of these parts that we are talking about.*

The question asked is, 'What fraction of this cake has icing (is shaded)?' We are talking about the shaded parts. There are 2 parts shaded so the top number is 2.

The fraction then is $^2/_5$.

Now ask pupils, *'What fraction of this cake does not have icing (is not shaded)?'*

Follow these steps.

Step 1 – *Draw the fraction bar (line separating the numerator and denominator).*

Step 2 – *The denominator (bottom number) tells us the number of equal sized parts a shape is divided (cut etc.) into. This cake is divided into 5 equal sized pieces so the bottom number is 5.*

Step 3 – *The numerator is the number of these parts that we are considering (talking about).*

The question asked is, 'What fraction of this cake does not have icing (is not shaded)?'

We are talking about the unshaded parts. There are 3 parts that are not shaded so the top number is 3.

The fraction then is $^3/_5$.

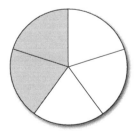

MATHS MASTERPIECES

Starry Night

Starry Night

MATHS MASTERPIECES

Down on His Luck

Background information

Down on His Luck

by Frederick McCubbin (1855 - 1917)

Frederick McCubbin was the son of an Australian baker. Recognising his son's talent, his father helped him get a job with a coachmaker where he painted decorations and crests on the coaches. McCubbin was unequalled at painting the Australian bush. His paintings usually had a story to tell, often of the hardships of rural life. This is shown in the expression and setting of *Down on His Luck*.

Internet image search

☞ *The Lost Child*

☞ *A Bush Burial*

☞ *On the Wallaby Track*

☞ *The Pioneer*

☞ *Winter Sunlight*

Pupil instructions

1. Cut out the tiles from the jigsaw sheet.

2. Work out the fraction questions on the backing board.

3. Match the numbers on the tiles to the answers on the backing board.

4. Glue the tiles onto their matching spaces.

5. Colour the picture in an interesting way.

Talking mathematically

Pupils should begin to relate fractions to division; for example,

- understand that finding $\frac{1}{2}$ is equivalent to dividing by 2, that finding $\frac{1}{4}$ is equivalent to dividing by 4,

  e.g. $\frac{1}{2}$ of 10 is equivalent to $10 \div 2$

  $\frac{1}{4}$ of 8 is equivalent to $8 \div 4$

- recognise that when 1 whole pizza is divided equally into 3, each person gets $\frac{1}{3}$,

  e.g. $1 \div 3 = \frac{1}{3}$

Down on His Luck

$\frac{1}{2}$ of 18	$\frac{1}{3}$ of 39	$\frac{1}{2}$ of 34	$\frac{1}{4}$ of 20
$\frac{1}{5}$ of 75	$\frac{1}{5}$ of 10	$\frac{1}{5}$ of 35	$\frac{1}{2}$ of 28
$\frac{1}{4}$ of 16	$\frac{1}{3}$ of 48	$\frac{1}{4}$ of 72	$\frac{1}{3}$ of 18
$\frac{1}{5}$ of 100	$\frac{1}{10}$ of 100	$\frac{1}{2}$ of 6	$\frac{1}{4}$ of 44
$\frac{1}{3}$ of 3	$\frac{1}{4}$ of 48	$\frac{1}{2}$ of 38	$\frac{1}{10}$ of 80

MATHS MASTERPIECES

Down on His Luck

Maths masterpieces

False Perspective

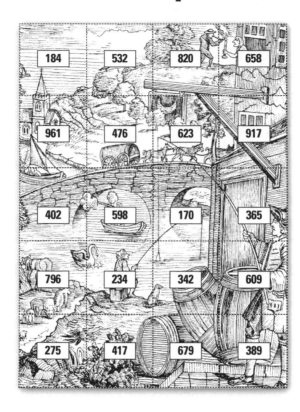

Background information

False Perspective

by William Hogarth (1697 – 1764)

An Englishman, Hogarth's career in art began as a book illustrator in 1720. He studied painting in his spare time. Hogarth was an entrepreneur and chose topics and themes that he knew would be popular with the art buying public.

His paintings often show things that were topical in his time. Many of his paintings satirise people's foibles.

Hogarth's purpose of creating the engraving *False Perspective* was to show how absurd it was for someone to attempt becoming an artist without having an understanding of perspective.

Internet image search

☞ *The Fishing Party*
☞ *The Theft of a Watch*
☞ *The Tavern Scene*
☞ *Sarah Malcom in Prison*
☞ *The Good Samaritan*
☞ *The Shrimp Girl*
☞ *Gin Lane*
☞ *Beer Street*
☞ *Shortly after the Marriage*

Pupil instructions

1. Cut out the tiles from the jigsaw sheet.
2. Write the number indicated by each description on the backing board.
3. Match the numbers on the tiles to the answers on the backing board.
4. Glue the tiles onto the matching spaces.
5. Colour the picture in an interesting way.

Talking mathematically

The Hindu-Arabic system (also called the decimal system) was popularised in Europe by the Italian mathematician Leonardo Fibonacci (1170 – 1250) who was also known as Leonardo of Pisa. Until that time, Roman numerals were used.

The decimal system uses ten digits (0 1 2 3 4 5 6 7 8 9) to write all numbers. Its basis is a system of place value where each column has a value that is ten times that immediately to its right. This holds true even with decimal fractions (decimals) where any number to the right of the decimal point has one-tenth of its value in the units column.

Unlike most number systems, the decimal system has a numeral for zero. Zero is used as a place holder in larger numbers.

MATHS MASTERPIECES

False Perspective

4 units 8 tens 1 hundred _____	3 tens 5 hundreds 2 units _____	0 units 2 tens 8 hundreds _____	5 tens 6 hundreds 8 units _____
60 + 1 + 900 _____	400 + 6 + 70 _____	3 + 600 + 20 _____	900 + 7 + 10 _____
(4 x 100) + (2 x 1) _____	(5 x 100) + (9 x 10) + (8 x 1) _____	(1 x 100) + (7 x 10) _____	(3 x 100) + (6 x 10) + (5 x 1) _____
700 90 + 6 _____	200 30 + 4 _____	300 40 + 2 _____	600 + 9 _____
7 tens + 5 units + 2 hundreds _____	10 + 400 + 7 _____	(6 x 100) + (7 x 10) + (9 x 1) _____	300 80 + 9 _____

Maths masterpieces

False Perspective

Teachers notes

MATHS MASTERPIECES

Vertumnus

Background information

Vertumnus

by Giuseppe Arcimboldo (1527 – 1593)

Arcimboldo was born in Milan, Italy in 1527. His father was also an artist and Giuseppe worked with him to paint Milan's cathedral.

He attracted the notice of Ferdinand I, the Emperor of Austria, and went to live in Vienna. He was very popular with the Austrian royal family. He began painting pictures made up of flowers, fruits and vegetables.

Vertumnus (the Roman God of vegetation) is a portrait of Austria's emperor Rudolph II.

Arcimboldo was just as creative with the spelling of his name. His pictures are variously signed Arcimboldo, Archimboldi and Archimboldus.

Internet image search

☞ *Air*   ☞ *Fire*

☞ *Earth*   ☞ *Water*

☞ *Spring*   ☞ *Summer*

☞ *Autumn*   ☞ *Winter*

☞ *The Cook*   ☞ *The Lawyer*

☞ *The Librarian*

☞ *The Vegetable Gardener*

☞ *Flora* (the Roman goddess of flowers and spring)

Additional activities

Discuss how the librarian is different from the other paintings on the Internet image search list.

Pupil instructions

1. Cut out the tiles from the jigsaw sheet.

2. Do the long multiplication sums on the backing board.

3. Match the numbers on the tiles to the answers on the backing board.

4. Glue the tiles onto their matching spaces.

5. Colour the picture in an interesting way.

Talking mathematically

Work through a number of examples using these steps.

Step 1 – Consider what 'question' the sum is 'asking'. We are being asked to find out how many 65 lots of 37 are altogether.

Step 2 – Multiply 65 by 7 and write the answer (455) on the third line.

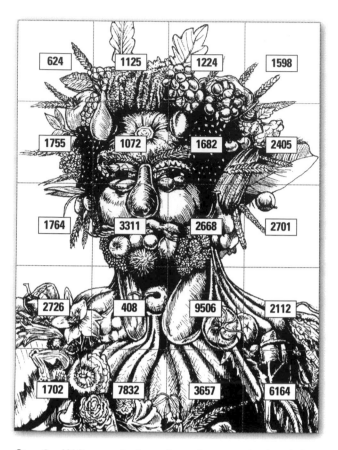

Step 3 – Write zero in the units column on the fourth line because the next number you are multiplying by is 30 (not 3). Do the multiplication by 3 and write the answer on the fourth line (1 950).

Step 4 – Add the two answers together and write the total on the bottom line (2 405).

It will be useful if pupils have some experience multiplying by multiples of 10; to 'prove' the 'write down zero' shortcut do some of these as additions. Pupils should accept the shortcut after doing a number of these; e.g. 20 x 40.

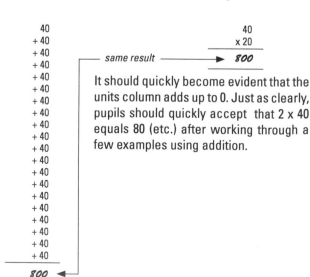

```
  40
+ 40
+ 40
+ 40
+ 40
+ 40
+ 40
+ 40
+ 40
+ 40
+ 40
+ 40
+ 40
+ 40
+ 40
+ 40
+ 40
+ 40
+ 40
+ 40
─────
 800
```

```
    40
  x 20
  ─────
   800
```

— *same result* ⟶ **800**

It should quickly become evident that the units column adds up to 0. Just as clearly, pupils should quickly accept that 2 x 40 equals 80 (etc.) after working through a few examples using addition.

Vertumnus

24 x 26	45 x 25	34 x 36	47 x 34
39 x 45	67 x 16	29 x 58	37 x 65
49 x 36	77 x 43	29 x 92	37 x 73
58 x 47	24 x 17	97 x 98	48 x 44
74 x 23	88 x 89	69 x 53	92 x 67

MATHS MASTERPIECES

Vertumnus

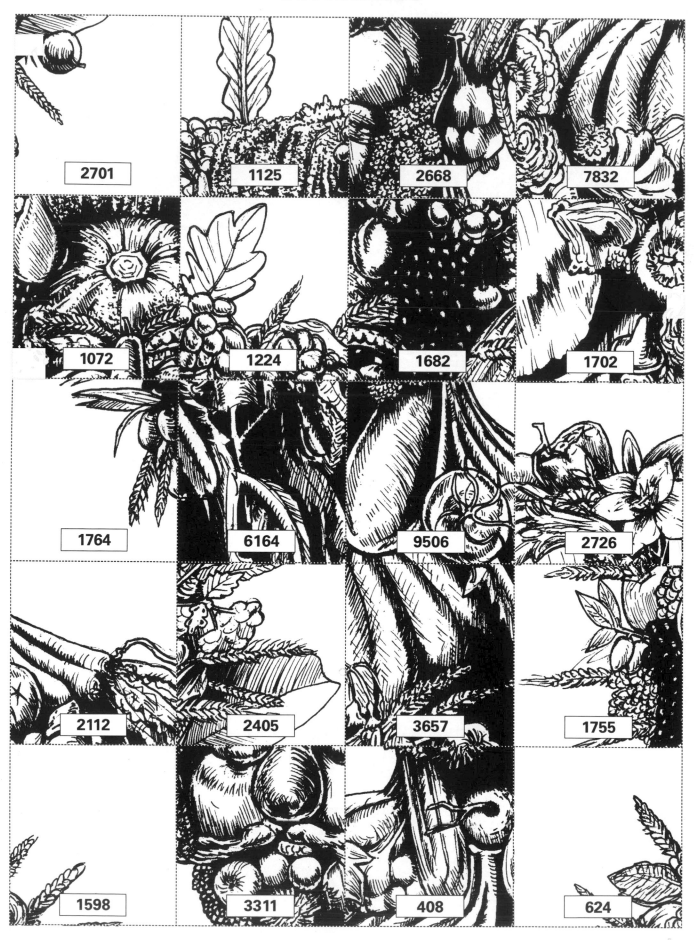

2701 | 1125 | 2668 | 7832

1072 | 1224 | 1682 | 1702

1764 | 6164 | 9506 | 2726

2112 | 2405 | 3657 | 1755

1598 | 3311 | 408 | 624